BRAIN ACADEMY MATHS

MISSION FILE 4
Charlotte Haggis, Louise Moore and Richard Cooper
Consultants for NACE: Elaine Sellars and Sue Lowndes
nace

RISING STARS

Rising Stars are grateful to the following people for their support in developing this series:
Sue Mordecai, Julie Fitzpatrick, Johanna Raffan and Belle Wallace.

nace

NACE, PO Box 242, Arnolds Way, Oxford, OX2 9FR
www.nace.co.uk

Rising Stars UK Ltd, 22 Grafton Street, London W1S 4EX
www.risingstars-uk.com

Published 2004
Reprinted 2005, 2006, 2007, 2008, 2009

Editorial: Charlotte Haggis, Louise Moore and Richard Cooper
Editorial Consultants: Elaine Sellars, Sue Lowndes and Sally Harbour
Design: Burville-Riley
Illustrations: Cover and insides – Sue Lee / Characters – Bill Greenhead
Cover design: Burville-Riley Design

British Library Cataloguing in Publication Data.
A CIP record for this book is available from the British Library.

ISBN: 978-1-904591-38-2

Printed by Craft Print International Limited, Singapore

CONTENTS

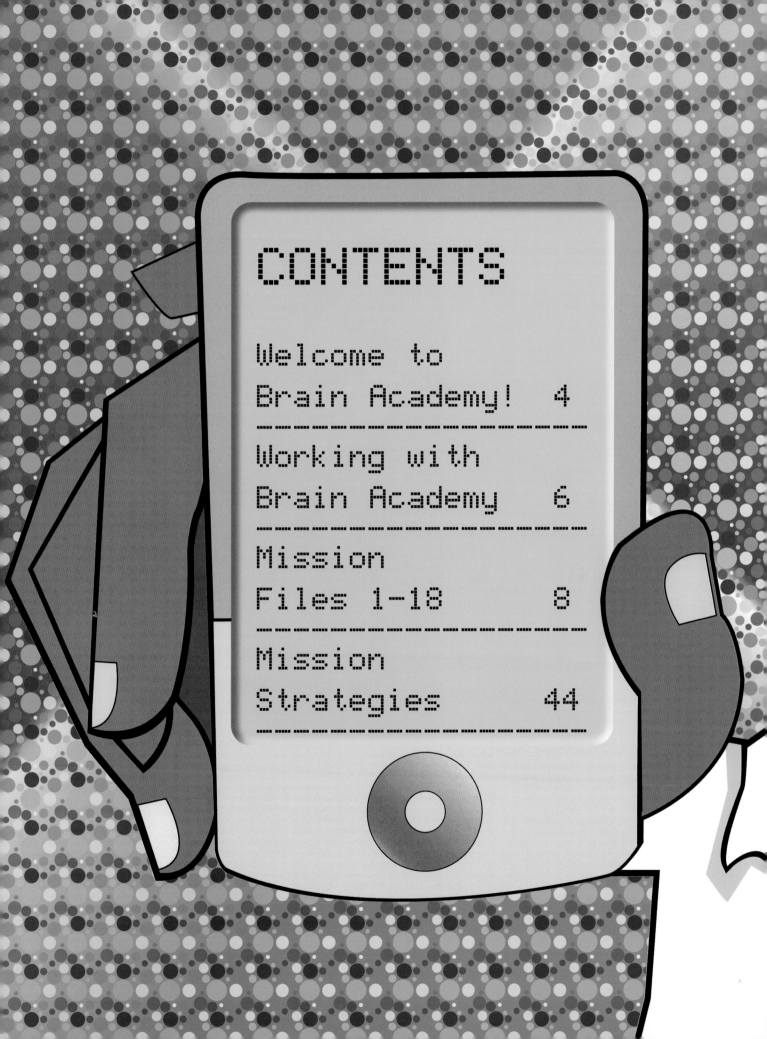

Welcome to Brain Academy!

Welcome to Brain Academy! Make yourself at home. We are here to give you the low-down on the organisation – so pay attention!
It's our job to help Da Vinci and his colleagues to solve the tough problems they face and we would like you to join us as members of the Academy. Are you up to the challenge?

Da Vinci

Da Vinci is the founder and head of the Brain Academy. He is all seeing, all thinking and all knowing – possibly the cleverest person alive. Nobody has ever actually seen him in the flesh as he communicates only via computer. When Da Vinci receives an emergency call for help, the members of Brain Academy jump into action (and that means you!).

Huxley

Huxley is Da Vinci's right-hand man. Not as clever, but still very smart. He is here to guide you through the missions and offer help and advice. The sensible and reliable face of Brain Academy, Huxley is cool under pressure.

Dr Hood

The mad doctor is the arch-enemy of Da Vinci and Brain Academy. He has set up a rival organisation called D.A.F.T. (which stands for Dull And Feeble Thinkers). Dr Hood and his agents will do anything they can to irritate and annoy the good people of this planet. He is a pain we could do without.

Hilary Kumar

Ms Kumar is the Prime Minister of our country. As the national leader she has a hotline through to the Academy but will only call in an extreme emergency. Confident and strong willed, she is a very tough cookie indeed.

General Cods-Wallop

This highly decorated gentleman (with medals, not wallpaper) is in charge of the armed forces. Most of his success has come from the help of Da Vinci and the Academy rather than the use of his somewhat limited military brain.

Mrs Tiggles

Stella Tiggles is the retired head of the Secret Intelligence service. She is a particular favourite of Da Vinci who treats her as his own mother. Mrs Tiggles' faithful companion is her cat, Bond... James Bond.

We were just like you once – ordinary schoolchildren leading ordinary lives. Then one day we all received a call from a strange character named Da Vinci. From that day on, we have led a double life – as secret members of Brain Academy!

Here are a few things you should know about the people you'll meet on your journey.

Maryland T. Wordsworth

M.T. Wordsworth is the president of the USA. Not the sharpest tool in the box, Maryland prefers to be known by his middle name, Texas, or 'Tex' for short. He takes great exception to being referred to as 'Mary' (which has happened in the past).

Buster Crimes

Buster is a really smooth dude and is in charge of the Police Force. His laid-back but efficient style has won him many friends, although these don't include Dr Hood or the agents of D.A.F.T. who regularly try to trick the coolest cop in town.

Sandy Buckett

The fearless Sandy Buckett is the head of the fire service. Sandy and her team of brave firefighters are always on hand, whether to extinguish the flames of chaos caused by the demented Dr Hood or just to rescue Mrs Tiggles' cat…

Echo the Eco-Warrior

Echo is the hippest chick around. Her love of nature and desire for justice will see her do anything to help an environmental cause – even if it means she's going to get her clothes dirty.

Victor Blastov

Victor Blastov is the leading scientist at the Space Agency. He once tried to build a rocket by himself but failed to get the lid off the glue. Victor often requires the services of the Academy, even if it's to set the video to record Dr Who.

Prince Barrington

Prince Barrington, or 'Bazza' as he is known to his friends, is the publicity-seeking heir to the throne. Always game for a laugh, the Prince will stop at nothing to raise money for worthy causes. A 'good egg' as his mother might say.

Working with Brain Academy

Do you get the idea? Now you've had the introduction we are going to show you the best way to use this book.

The plot

This tells you what the mission is about.

The Training Mission

Huxley will give you some practice before sending you on the main mission.

MISSION FILE 4:6

A 'brief challenge' for Prince Barrington

Time: High noon
Place: Prince Barrington's mansio

Prince Barrington has agreed to do a sponsored skate for one of his favourite worthwhile causes – the Pupils Against National Tests Society (P.A.N.T.S.).

He has promised to rollerskate to different schools wearing only his underpants. The more schools he reaches, the more earplugs he will earn for P.A.N.T.S. To collect enough earplugs to block the ears of all the pupils he needs the help of... Brain Academy!

How long is the shortest route Prince Barrington can take if he visits each fountain at least once? You can start and finish at any fountain.

18

Each mission is divided up into different parts.
No one said this was easy. In fact that is why you have been chosen. Da Vinci will only take the best and he believes that includes you. Good luck!

Each book contains a number of 'missions' for you to take part in. You will work with the characters in Brain Academy to complete these missions.

The Main Mission

This is where you try to complete the challenge.

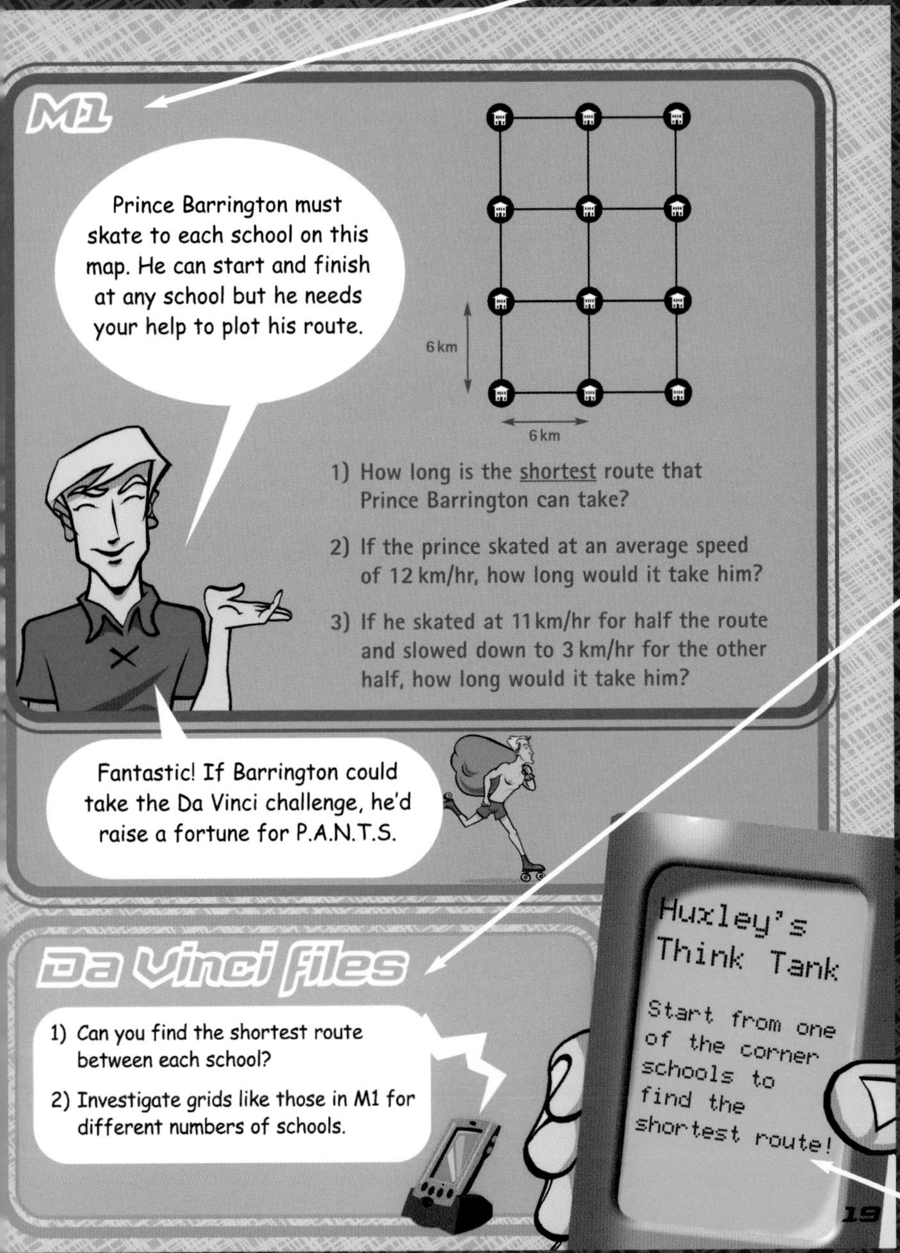

M1

Prince Barrington must skate to each school on this map. He can start and finish at any school but he needs your help to plot his route.

6 km

6 km

1) How long is the <u>shortest</u> route that Prince Barrington can take?
2) If the prince skated at an average speed of 12 km/hr, how long would it take him?
3) If he skated at 11 km/hr for half the route and slowed down to 3 km/hr for the other half, how long would it take him?

Fantastic! If Barrington could take the Da Vinci challenge, he'd raise a fortune for P.A.N.T.S.

Da Vinci files

1) Can you find the shortest route between each school?
2) Investigate grids like those in M1 for different numbers of schools.

Huxley's Think Tank

Start from one of the corner schools to find the shortest route!

19

The Da Vinci Files

These problems are for the best Brain Academy recruits. Very tough. Are you tough enough?

Huxley's Think Tank

Huxley will download some useful tips onto your PDA to help you on each mission.

PS: See pages 44–47 for a useful process and hints and tips!

A 'Daft' potion!

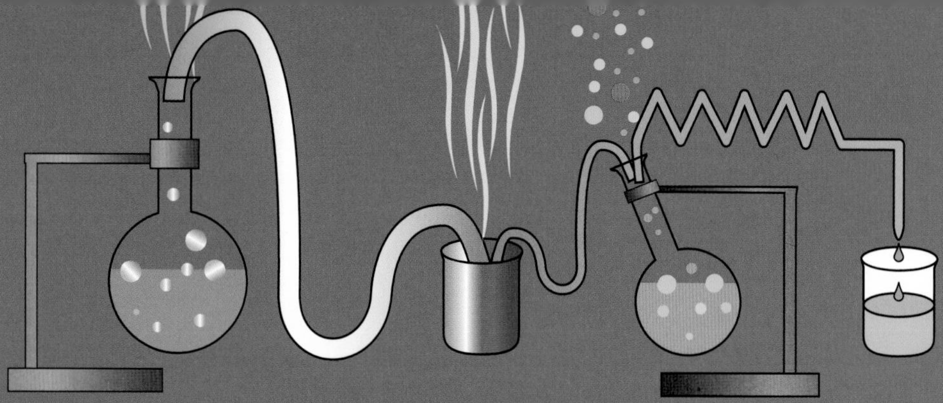

Time: Elevenses
Place: Hilary's kitchen

Dr Hood is causing havoc across the country. He has concocted a secret potion that will send anyone who consumes it into a very deep and very long sleep so he can irritate the nation without being disturbed. Hilary Kumar sees it as her job to try and stop him!

What do I do, Da Vinci?
Keep yourself awake for Huxley's Training Mission, Hilary!

TM

I have some recipes for sleeping potion antidotes. If you can work out what ingredients to buy you'll solve the training mission!

To make 60g of SLEEP STOP you need:
- TWO eggs (of equal weight)
- Mud (weighing the same as the eggs)
- The same weight in jam as the mud

1) What weight of jam will you need?
2) What weight of mud will you need?
3) What is the weight of ONE egg?

To make 220g of WAKE-UP WAFFLES you need:
- TWO sausages (of equal weight)
- Porridge
- Compost
- Pond sludge

Each ingredient weighs the same as TWO sausages.

4) What is the weight of ONE sausage?
5) How much porridge will you need?

M1

Hilary has found the formula that Dr Hood is using to send people to sleep. Answering these questions will allow Hilary to know how much of her antidote to use on the victims.

To make 18 litres of SWEET DREAM JUICE you need to:
Measure 4 jugs of spider spit. Next, measure exactly the same quantity of panda perspiration. Stir in the same quantity (4 jugs) of seawater. Now add the same quantity of 'Bestgo's Dream Medicine'. Mix these together with a fork or whisk.

1) How much spider spit is needed?

2) How many litres of liquid in one jug of panda perspiration?

3) How many jugs of 'Bestgo's Dream Medicine' will be needed to make 36 litres of SWEET DREAM JUICE?

If Hilary can complete the Da Vinci Challenge, she'll be able to use her antidote to wake up Britain... just in time for some morning television.

Da Vinci files

1) Hilary has made a new quantity of SWEET DREAM JUICE to test. She put ONE litre of the juice into each of the NINE bottles. How many jugs of spider spit went into the potion?

2) The next time she made some potion she put FOUR litres into each of the NINE bottles. How much spider spit did she use?

Huxley's Think Tank

The fact that there is the same amount of most of the ingredients will help you divide the total capacity/mass accordingly!

Earth-shattering news for Sandy!

Time: Dusk
Place: Tremor Town

There has been a terrible earthquake in Tremor Town and falling debris has caused families to become trapped in their homes. Sandy Buckett has arrived on the scene to help free the petrified people.

Da Vinci, I'm feeling very shaky about this challenge, help!

You'll be on more solid ground once you've done Huxley's Training Mission!

TM

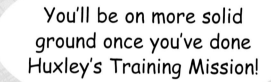

We need to get TEN firefighters to the scene of the earthquake. You'll need to decide how many male firefighters and how many female firefighters are going to travel in each engine.

In the first engine, fireman Sam was joined by some helpers. There was ONE more man than there were women.

In the second engine there were FOUR times as many men than ladies. How many firefighters in each engine?

M1

The firefighters soon arrive on the scene. It seems that there are a lot of children in the families who have been trapped. Can you help Sandy and her crew find out how many children they need to save from each household?

1) Mr and Mrs Berry have a large number of children.
   Kerry, the youngest daughter has FIVE more brothers than sisters.
   Her elder brother Perry has HALF as many sisters as brothers.
   How many children in the Berry family?

2) Mr and Mrs Doe also have a large number of children.
   Mo, the youngest daughter has TWO more sisters than brothers.
   Her elder brother Joe has THREE times as many sisters as brothers.
   How many siblings in the Doe family?

3) Mr and Mrs Trickie have lots of children.
   Ricky, the oldest of the siblings, has THREE times as many sisters as brothers.
   Vicky, his younger sister has HALF as many brothers as sisters.
   How many children in the Trickie family?

Earth-shattering work! If Sandy can take the Da Vinci Challenge there will be a happy ending to this eventful day.

Da Vinci files

Sandy became very confused that Perry Berry, Terry Berry, Kerry Berry and Gerry Berry had nicknames. Their nicknames are Pixie, Fluffy, Zippy and Beanie. Can you help her work out who is who?

1) Fluffy loves to go to the cinema with Zippy and Gerry.
2) Perry sometimes argues with Beanie.
3) Terry used to go swimming with Beanie and Zippy.
4) Kerry likes to go out for long walks with Zippy, Fluffy and Beanie.

Huxley's Think Tank
First write all the names down. In a fire always ask for a sandy bucket to put out the flames.

MISSION FILE 4:3

Echo shows she has bottle!

Time: 10.30 am
Place: Trash Town

The people of Trash Town are feeling very gloomy because of the amount of used cans and bottles that litter the pretty streets. Echo decides that it's time to show that she has bottle by facing up to the council and asking them to put some recycling banks around the area.

What 'can' I do, Da Vinci?
Start 'banking' some answers with Huxley's Training Mission!

TM

Help Echo decide if recyling bins have been a success.

For every SIX bottles that were recycled, there were EIGHT cans recycled.

1) If 72 cans were recycled, how many bottles were put in the bank?
2) If 78 bottles were recycled, how many cans went into the can bank?

For every NINE magazines that were recycled, there were TWELVE newspapers.

3) If 96 newspapers were recycled during the trial period, how many magazines were put into the paper bank?
4) If 126 magazines were put into the paper bank, how many newspapers were recycled?

M1

The trial was a success and a number of bins have been installed in Trash Town. Can you work out how many of each type have been fitted?

Bottle banks are SIX metres long and can banks are FOUR metres long. Altogether the combined length of all the recycling bins in Trash Town is 46 metres.

1) If there is at least ONE bottle bank and ONE can bank, how many bottle and can banks are there? Find TWO different answers.

   In the nearby village of Debris Dales the combined length of the new recycling bins is 58 metres.

2) How many bottle and can banks are there?

3) Can you find FIVE possible answers?

If Echo can solve Da Vinci's Challenge, Trash Town will be an environmentally friendly town!

Da Vinci files

Binnit village decided to install a 3 metre paper-recycling bank.

If there was at least one bottle, one can and one paper bank and the combined length of all the recyling banks is 52 metres, what possible combinations of recycling bins could be in Binnit Village?

Huxley's Think Tank
Think in multiples. Working out all the possible total lengths of can banks will give you a starting point!

MISSION FILE 4:4

Cat-astrophe for Echo!

Time: Teatime
Place: Rushmore Safari Park

Rushmore Safari Park has a problem with two of its most savage tigers, Chicken and Chips. Chicken and Chips are running wild and trying to eat up all the visitors. The zookeeper has asked for the help of Echo the Eco-Warrior.

RUSHMORE

Help, Da Vinci, this challenge is driving me wild!

Huxley's Training Mission will give you something to get your teeth into!

TM

The zookeeper gives Echo eight sets of bars. FOUR of the bars are 10 m and FOUR of the bars are 5 m long. By answering these questions Echo should be able to cage these wild beasts.

1) How can Echo arrange the bars to make TWO square pens?

2) How can she arrange them to make FOUR square pens?

M1

If you can answer these questions, it will mean that Echo will be able to create a secure home for the cats. The zoo-keeper gives Echo 48 km of electric fencing to build some pens.

1) Chicken is a very fat tiger and needs the biggest pen possible. Chips is only a small cub so needs the smallest pen possible. How would Echo make TWO pens that have the largest and smallest areas possible, where each side is a complete number of km?

2) What could the lengths of the sides be if Echo makes TWO pens, both with an area of 32 km^2? Each side is a complete number of km.

3) How can Echo make NINE identical square pens, where each side is a complete number of km? What is the perimeter of one of the squares?

Grrrrreat work! Get past the Da Vinci challenge and Chicken and Chips will never scare the public again.

Da Vinci files

Echo makes TWO identical right-angled triangular pens. What shapes can she make by combining the TWO pens?

Huxley's Think Tank
Don't worry about what the bars are made out of. Always think about patterns when you look at the questions.

Eat your greens, Echo!

Time: Dinner time
Place: A cabbage patch in Wales

Echo the Eco-Warrior has travelled to Wales to fight another ecological battl
The local caterpillars are eating the last remaining purple-stemmed cabbag
plants in the world. There is only one cabbage patch left to fence off before
the purple-stemmed variety becomes extinct!

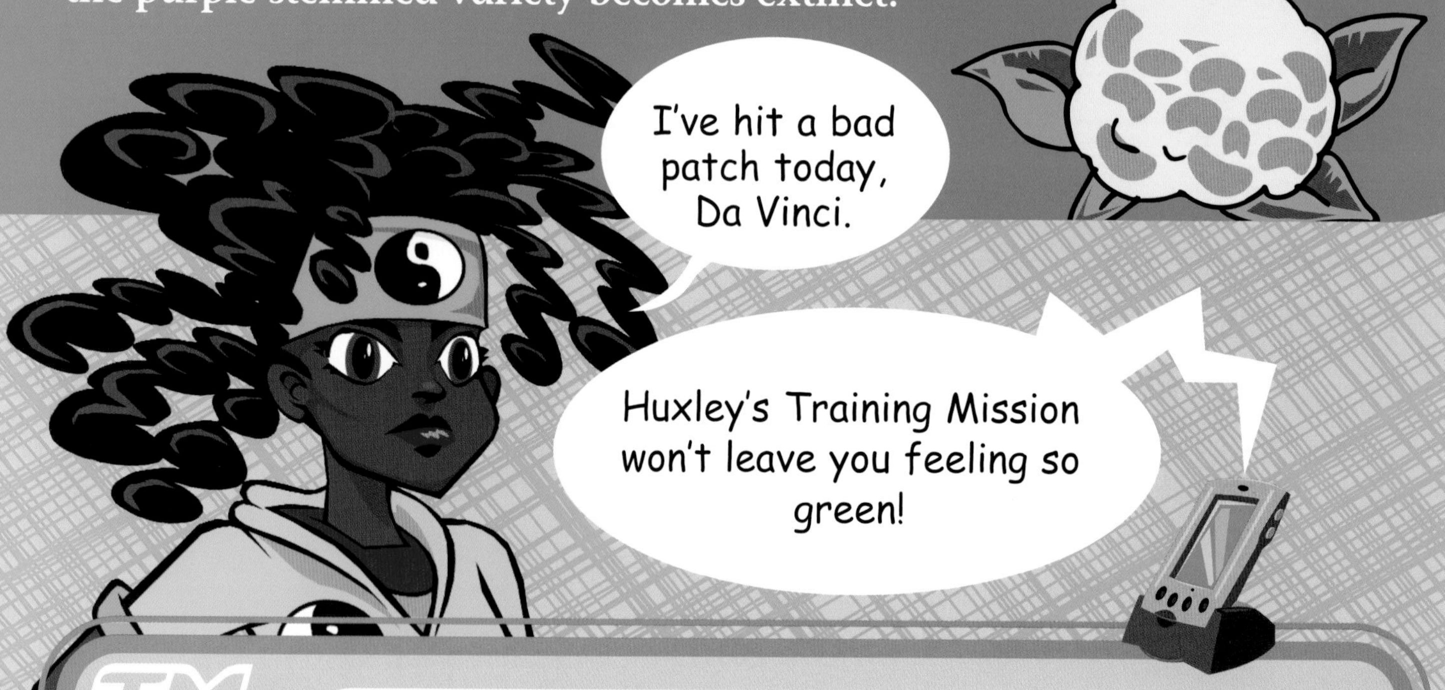

I've hit a bad patch today, Da Vinci.
Huxley's Training Mission won't leave you feeling so green!

TM

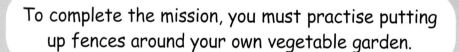

To complete the mission, you must practise putting up fences around your own vegetable garden.

1) Echo fences off a rectangular plot with a perimeter of 24 m. The longer sides of the vegetable patch are twice the length of the shorter sides. How much fencing will Echo need for each shorter side?

2) She also fences off a rectangular plot with a perimeter of 30 m. The longer sides of the vegetable patch are twice the length of the shorter sides. How much fencing will Echo need for each shorter side?

M1

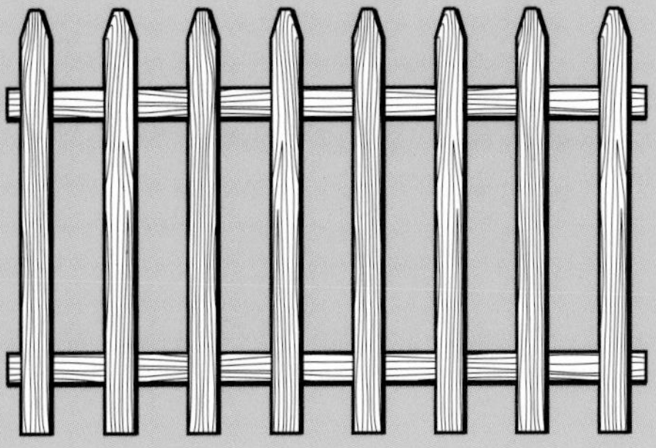

Echo is now ready to leave for Wales to fence off those cabbages. She takes some panels of fencing with her. The panels are the following lengths:

16m   10m   8m   6m   6m   2m

1) Can you help Echo use all the fence panels to make a rectangle?

2) Can Echo make a different rectangle?

3) What other shapes can Echo make with all the fence panels?

If Echo can master the Da Vinci Challenge the cabbages will keep growing forever!

Da Vinci files

There are 225 cabbages left. Each caterpillar eats THREE cabbages each day. Every day another caterpillar hatches. If Echo didn't get her fence up, how many days would it take for the caterpillars to eat all the cabbages if there were THREE caterpillars to begin with?

Huxley's Think Tank

Using different length straws might help you. You might find it helpful to record your ideas on squared paper.

A 'brief challenge' for Prince Barrington

Time: High noon
Place: Prince Barrington's mansion

Prince Barrington has agreed to do a sponsored skate for one of his favourite worthwhile causes – the Pupils Against National Tests Society (P.A.N.T.S.).

He has promised to rollerskate to different schools wearing only his underpants. The more schools he reaches, the more earplugs he will earn for P.A.N.T.S. To collect enough earplugs to block the ears of all the pupils he needs the help of... Brain Academy!

It's jolly cold out here. Da Vinci, where do I begin?
You can start raising money if you complete the Training Mission Huxley has designed.

TM

OK, Prince Barrington, let's get you warmed up! Firstly you need to skate around your garden – and mind you don't end up in the ornamental pond!

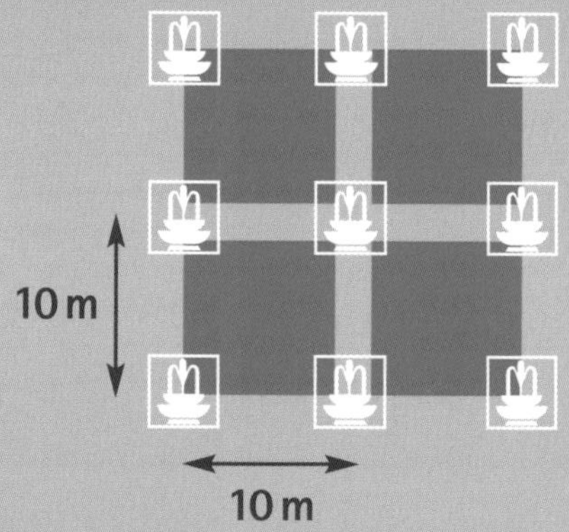

10 m
10 m

How long is the <u>shortest</u> route Prince Barrington can take if he visits each fountain at least once? You can start and finish at any fountain.

M1

Prince Barrington must skate to each school on this map. He can start and finish at any school but he needs your help to plot his route.

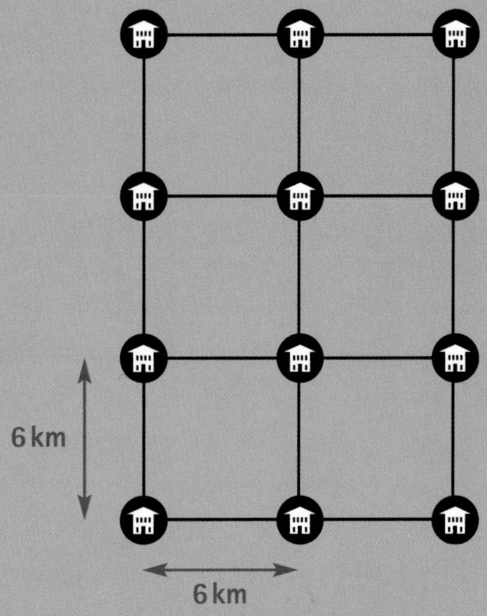

1) How long is the shortest route that Prince Barrington can take?
2) If the prince skated at an average speed of 12 km/hr, how long would it take him?
3) If he skated at 11 km/hr for half the route and slowed down to 3 km/hr for the other half, how long would it take him?

Fantastic! If Barrington could take the Da Vinci challenge, he'd raise a fortune for P.A.N.T.S.

Da Vinci files

1) Can you find the shortest route between each school?
2) Investigate grids like those in M1 for different numbers of schools.

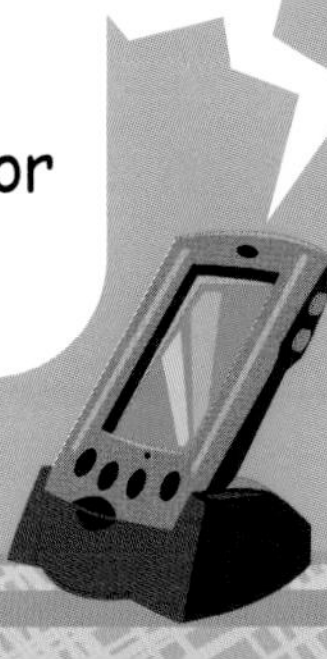

Rocket science

Time: Early afternoon
Place: NASA headquarters

Victor Blastov has a terrible problem! He needs to launch his spaceship next week and the blast-ed thing just will not start! He needs the help of Brain Academy!

Can you help me get this project off the ground, Da Vinci?
Huxley's Training Mission will get you off to a flying start!

TM

If you are going to fix the rocket, you'll need to find the numbers of the faulty engine parts.

1) The first engine part has a number that is a two-digit, odd multiple of FIVE and the sum of the digits is EIGHT. What is the number?
2) Find the number of the second engine part if it is an even factor of 84 between 20 and 30.
3) Calculate the third engine number if it is the sum of the first five prime numbers.

M1

It's time for Victor to call for help! Can you help Victor to hand out the equipment that his willing helpers will need to repair the rocket?

The mechanics will need 28 spanners to fix the faulty rocket. All the mechanics have at least one spanner. The three mechanics share out the spanners. Each mechanic has a different even number of spanners.

1) How many could they have each?
   Find all TEN possible solutions.

The rocket still won't work, so Victor asks three old ladies to whack it with their walking sticks. The THREE pensioners have a total of 37 walking sticks. Each pensioner has a different odd number of sticks.

2) How many do they have each?
   Find all possible solutions.

If Victor can solve the Da Vinci Challenge his rocket might just make it to Mars after all.

Da Vinci files

The rocket seems to be working. Victor thinks that a half-hour test flight will ensure that all is well. FOUR astronauts share the piloting. Each astonaut pilots for an even number of minutes and THREE of them pilot for exactly the same length of time.
How many solutions can you find?

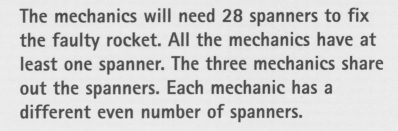

Huxley's Think Tank
Write down each fact that you know.
It doesn't matter how long the walking sticks are!

An eggs-traordinary challenge for Echo

Time: Before lunch
Place: A tree in the USA

President Maryland T Wordsworth of the USA is very worried that numbers of the rare and beautiful 'Bullet Hawk' bird are plummeting. Echo the Eco-Warrior has agreed to monitor the birds closely and plan how they could be bred in captivity.

This really is egg-citing Da Vinci, where do I begin?

First complete Huxley's Training Mission.

TM

OK Echo, we need to count the 'Bullet Hawks' to see if this problem is as serious as we think.

1) Echo carefully counts the birds.
When she counted them in 3s she had 2 left over.
When she counted them in 7s she had 3 left over.
She counted less than 30 birds, how many birds did she count?

2) She decides to count the birds again.
When she counted them in 8s she had 7 left over.
When she counted them in 9s she had 2 left over.
She counted less than 50 birds, how many birds did she count this time?

M1

Echo will need to count the number of eggs that 'Bullet Hawk' birds lay if she is going to help to successfully breed them in captivity. She's having a bit of trouble and she needs your help!

Echo counts the first bird's eggs. When she counted them in 7s she had 6 left over. When she counted them in 4s she had 1 left over.

1) She counted less than 100, how many did she count?
   Find TWO possible answers.

She carefully counts the eggs in the second bird's nest. When she counted them in 5s she had 3 left over. When she counted them in 3s she had 1 left over.

2) She counted less than 100 eggs, how many did she count?
   Find SIX possible answers.

If Echo can complete the Da Vinci Challenge, the number of Bullet Hawk birds will soar!

Da Vinci files

Echo collects some eggs, which will be hatched by some local zoos. She gives half the quantity to The American National Zoo. She then gives TWO of the eggs to a local bird group. She gives half the remainder to The National Wildlife Park. She gives ONE egg to the Manager of the Park. She gives half the remainder to the US Bird Park. She then gives the owner of the Bird Park an extra TWO eggs. Echo has THREE eggs left. How many did she start with?

Huxley's Think Tank

You have got to think about different multiples. Write out the tables and see if you get any clues.

It's 'snow' joke!

Time: Mid-morning
Place: By the sea

Dr Hood is using his latest invention to ruin the summer fun of holiday makers on the Isle of Chilly by blasting them with ice-cold snow. Sandy Buckett sees it as her job to stop this villain and his 'Snow Maker' making millions of people cold and miserable. Sandy is unsure how to get to the island, though … she needs to call Brain Academy!

This is 'snow' joke, Da Vinci!
Huxley has a Training Mission that will get you warmed up!

TM

You need to make a start on stopping the 'Snow Maker'. Sandy is deciding how to get some friends across to the island to help her.

ONE man and TWO boys need to cross the sea in a dinghy. They can all paddle but the dinghy will only hold ONE man or TWO boys.

How do they all get to the Isle of Chilly?

M1

Sandy is going to need more help if she is to stop this weather disaster. Can you help her get some more of her friends to the 'Isle of Chilly' and stop Dr Hood's fun?

1) ONE man and THREE boys need to cross the sea, in a dinghy. They can all paddle but the dinghy will only hold one man or two boys. How do they all get to the island?

2) a) TWO men and TWO boys need to cross the sea in a dinghy. They can all paddle but the dinghy will only hold ONE man or TWO boys. How do they all get to the island?
   b) If it takes two hours to row to the island, how long will it take for the group to get there?

Completing the Da Vinci Challenge will ensure Sandy can arrive on the island ready to take action!

Da Vinci files

It is 60km from the mainland to the island.

1) If TWO men and TWO boys had TWO dinghies, how do they all get over to the island?

2) If they row at 20km per hour how long will it take to get them all to the island?

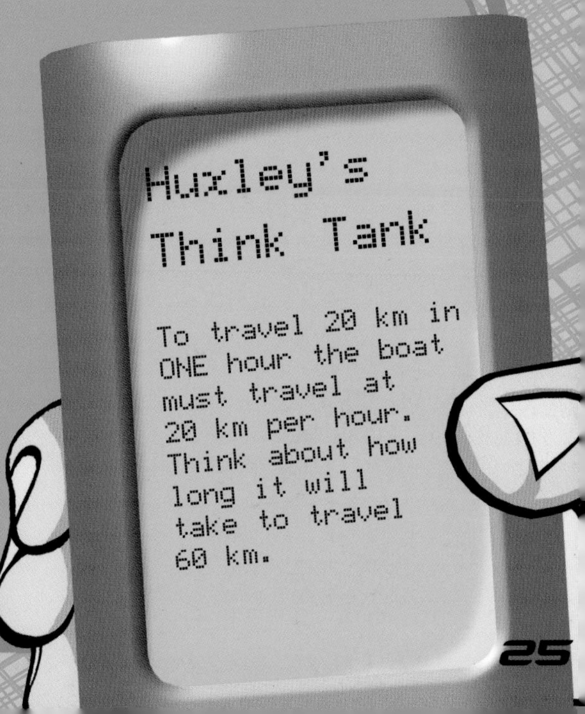

Huxley's Think Tank
To travel 20 km in ONE hour the boat must travel at 20 km per hour. Think about how long it will take to travel 60 km.

MISSION FILE 4:10

Musical chairs

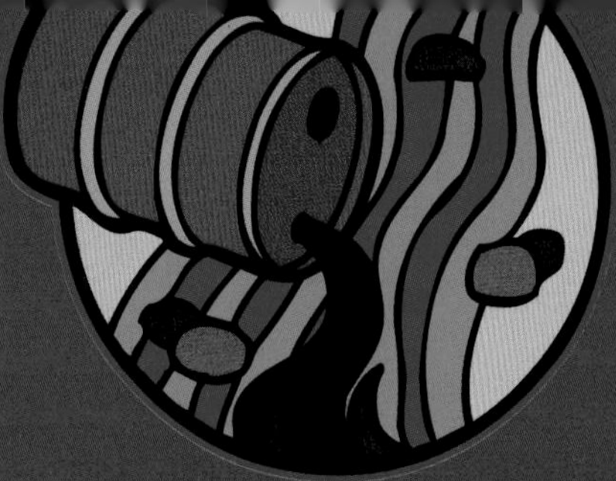

Time: Question time!
Place: The House of Commons

Growing levels of pollution in our rivers and seas are having disastrous consequences throughout the world! The Prime Minister, Hilary Kumar, has decided that some action must be taken. She calls an emergency meeting and invites all the world leaders.

Da Vinci, what must I do to save our planet?
Complete the Training Mission to get the presidents seated.

TM

President Maryland T Wordsworth of the U.S.A and President Frank French of France have joined Hilary at the meeting. They are invited to sit at a circular table.

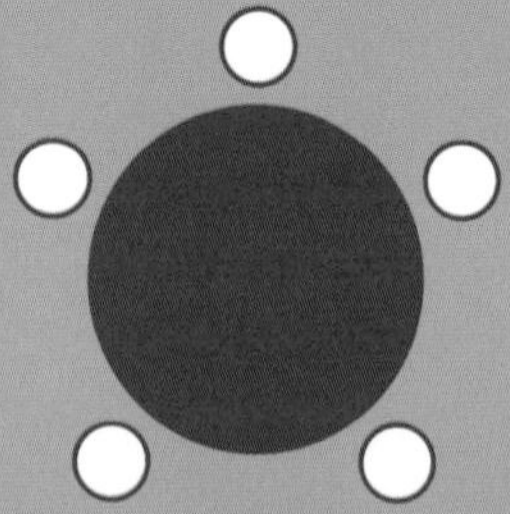

1) How many ways are there that the TWO visitors can sit around a table with FIVE chairs?

2) How about if there are SEVEN chairs?

M1

Just as the meeting is due to start, TWO more presidents arrive from Russia and Greece. Hilary now has the job of seating them too. Can you help her?

1) How many ways are there that the TWO people can sit around a table with SIX chairs?

2) Can you work out how many ways there are that THREE people would be able to sit round a table with SIX chairs?

3) Can you work out how many ways there are that FOUR people can sit around a table with SIX chairs?

Completing the Da Vinci Challenge will mean that the meeting can get started and a solution can be found!

Da Vinci files

The president of Japan arrives and the six presidents sit at this table:

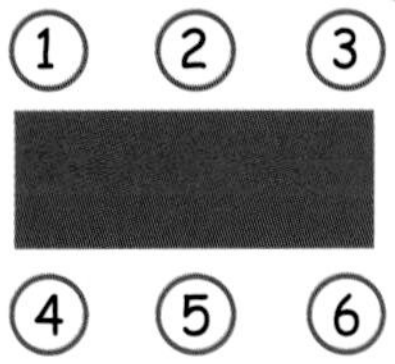

The British president sits in seat three. The president of the USA is opposite the president of Greece, who has the president of France on his left. The president of Japan is between the presidents of Russia and the USA. Work out who sat where.

Huxley's Think Tank
You may find it useful to label the chairs using letters.

A cracker of a code

Time: Coffee time
Place: The Police Station

Dr Hood has given each of his agents their own secret D.A.F.T. I.D. and agent number. He can use his code to work out an agent number for each of his agents based on their own personal D.A.F.T. I.D.. Then his agents can create havoc and their real names will be kept secret.

Buster Crimes plans to crack the code?

I won't crack under pressure, Da Vinci. Where shall I start?
Huxley's Training Mission will have you cracking codes in no time.

TM

Dr Hood treats the numbers and letters individually. He works out the value of each letter and adds this to the total value of the digits.

Here is some of his code:

A	B	C	D	E	F	G	H	I	J	K	L	M	N
7	12	8	15	19	24	5	26	17	1	25	13	21	23

e.g. D.A.F.T. I.D. AJ26BL

$2 + 6 = 8$

$7 + 1 + 2 + 6 + 12 + 13 = 41$

1) Find the number of the agent with the code FJ41362NA.

2) Clifford Able's D.A.F.T. I.D. is CH22131MP. Clifford Able is agent 66. Find the value of P.

M1

Some letters are a little more tricky to find. Help Buster work out as many values as you can.

1) Agent number 70 has the code WW51525ID. Find the value of W.

2) The agent with the code BE44216UK has a number FOUR more than the agent with the code BE44216AK. Find the value of U.

3) The agent with the code HI12321AM has a number EIGHT more than the agent with the code HI41251AR. Find the value of R.

Once Buster has completed the Da Vinci Challenge, Dr Hood will never get a code past him again!

Da Vinci files

Agent TX51322BC has the number 51. Work out the values of T and X if T is greater than X.

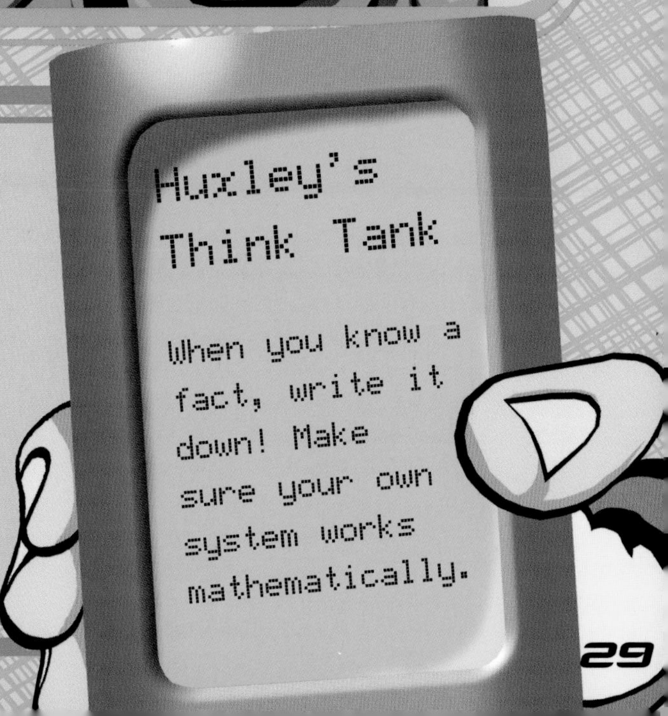

Huxley's Think Tank
When you know a fact, write it down! Make sure your own system works mathematically.

Wire worries for Victor

Time: A bit before lunch
Place: NASA headquarters

Victor Blastov is putting the finishing touches to his manned spaceship. He has decided that he really needs some headlights, as he thinks it could be dark up there. Unfortunately he isn't very good at the electrical wiring this creates. He needs to call Brain Academy!

I hope I'm able to sort my wiring issues, Da Vinci.
Let's see if you can shine with the Training Mission that Huxley has planned for you.

TM

Help Victor to get the front lights working by answering these questions.

1) If Victor cuts a piece of wire 2 cm long and then another piece 4 cm long with every piece after that being 2 cm longer than the last, what is the total length of wire cut after FIVE snips?

2) If Victor keeps doing this, what will the total length of wire cut be after he has made TEN snips?

M1

The front lights are now working. Completing the next questions will get those back lights beaming!

1) Victor cuts a piece of wire 3 cm long. Every piece of wire he cuts after this is always 3 cm longer than the last piece. If he cuts 20 pieces of wire, what will the total length of the cut pieces be?

2) Victor cuts another piece of wire 4 cm long. Every piece of wire he cuts after this is always 4 cm longer than the last piece. If he cuts 20 pieces of wire, what will the total length cut be?

3) Victor cuts another piece of wire 5 cm long. Every piece of wire he cuts after this is always 5 cm longer than the last piece. If he cuts 20 pieces of wire, what will the total length cut be?

Dazzling work! Completing this Da Vinci Challenge will ensure that Victor's headlights remain on.

Da Vinci files

Look at the answers you have found in Mission 1 and spot the pattern. Can you make a rule from this? Use your rule to find the total length of wire cut after 20 cuts if the first cut is 90 cm and all the cuts after that are 90 cm longer than the last.

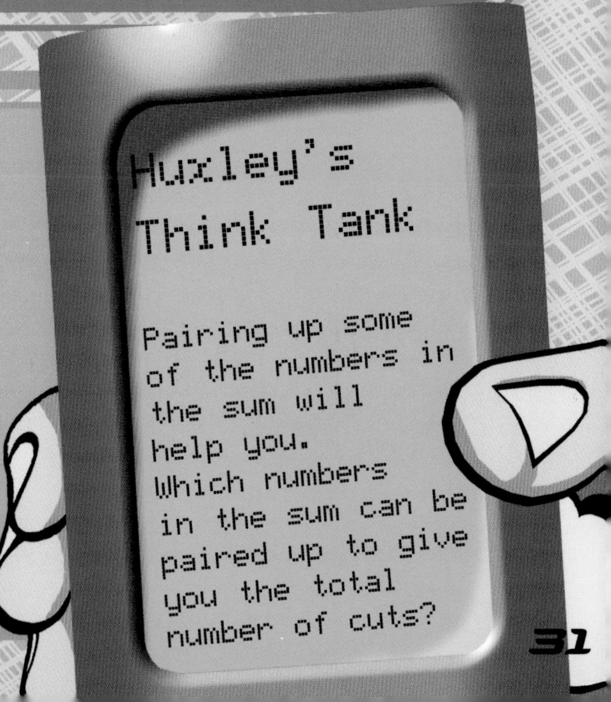

Huxley's Think Tank
Pairing up some of the numbers in the sum will help you.
Which numbers in the sum can be paired up to give you the total number of cuts?

A pacey PC!

Time: After breakfast
Place: Buster Crimes's car

On Monday, Police Commissioner Crimes needs to drive to the scene of a burglary. The problem is he doesn't know the best way to get there. It's time for Brain Academy to step in and give him some direction!

TM

You need to get your bearings first. Help Buster by working through these navigational questions.

1) How many kilometres is the shortest distance from Buster's house to the scene of the crime?

2) How many ways are there that he can travel this distance?

3) How many routes can you find which are longer (without retracing your steps)?

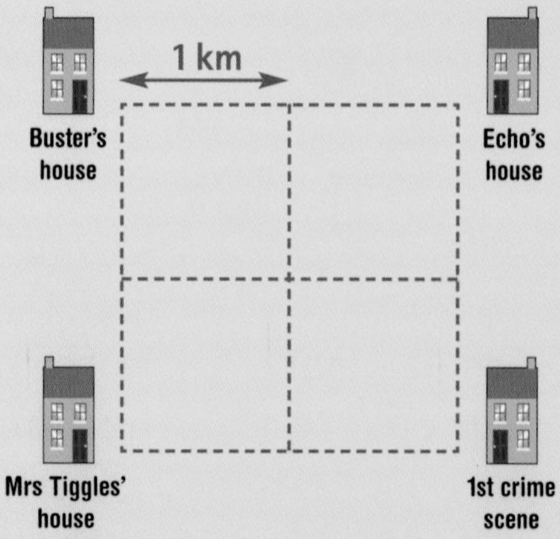

M1

On Wednesday Buster has to leave his house to visit another crime scene.

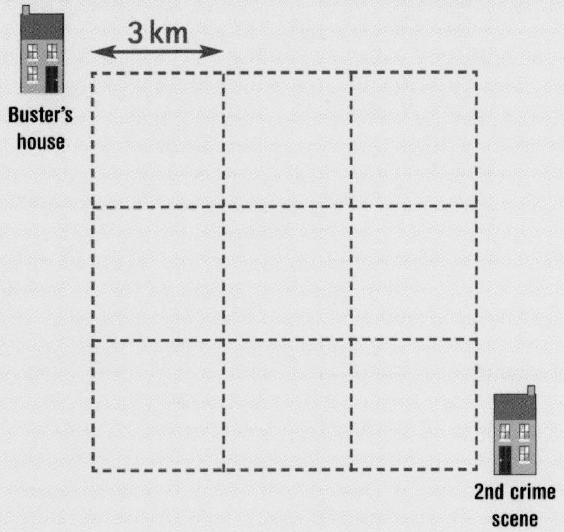

1) What is the shortest distance he can travel to the incident?

2) How many other routes are there that are this distance?

3) What are the other distances that Buster might travel if he doesn't retrace his steps?

Completing the Da Vinci Challenge will ensure that Buster arrives in the right place to investigate Wednesday's crime.

Da Vinci files

Buster walks to the scene of Wednesday's crime.

1) He walks at 6 km per hour. If he takes the shortest route, how long will his journey take?
2) Buster jogs home from the crime scene, using the shortest route, in two hours. What speed was he jogging at?

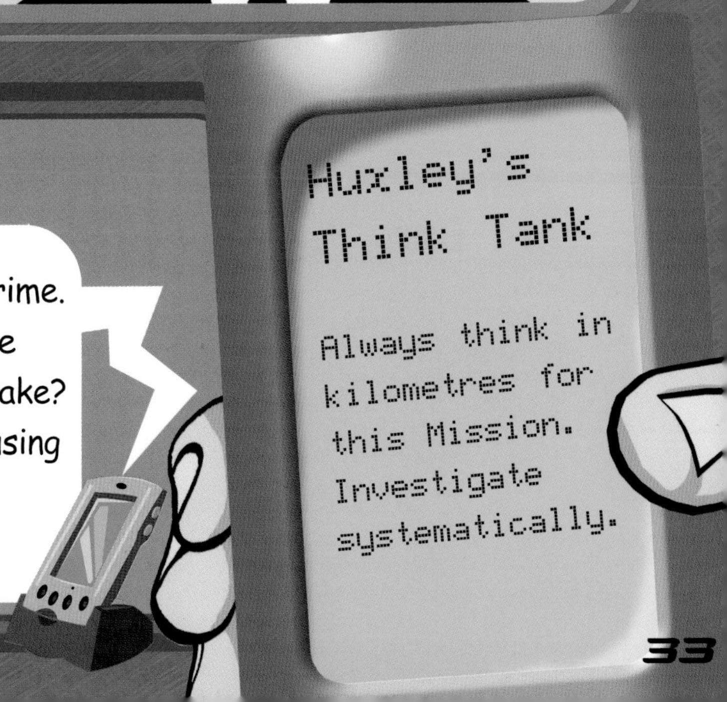

Huxley's Think Tank

Always think in kilometres for this Mission. Investigate systematically.

MISSION FILE 4:14

Sandy gets sandy!

Time: Midday
Place: At the beach

A group of D.A.F.T. agents are attempting to ruin the sandcastle-building fun of holidaymakers by paving over the beaches of Britain. Firefighter Sandy has grabbed her Buckett and headed off to the coast to stop them.

It would 'a-pier' that we have a problem, Da Vinci.

Huxley's Training Mission will get you digging for the right clues!

TM

If you can complete your Training Mission you'll have enough concrete evidence to get those villains locked up!

3 m x 3 m

4 m x 4 m

8 m x 8 m

THREE agents are at one end of the beach. They are laying slabs in lines. All THREE agents start laying the slabs so that each of the first slabs are in a line. One agent is laying paving slabs that are 3 m x 3 m, another has 4 m x 4 m slabs and the third agent has slabs that are 8 m x 8 m.

1) If they keep laying the slabs, what distance will have been covered before they are in line again?

2) How many slabs will the agent with the smallest square slabs have laid?

M1

Now FOUR D.A.F.T. agents stand in a line at one end of the beach. One agent is laying paving slabs that are 8 m x 8 m, another has 7m x 7m slabs, the third agent has slabs that are 4 m x 4 m and the fourth agent has slabs that are 14 m x 14 m.

1) If they keep laying their slabs, how far will they have gone before they are in line again?

2) How many slabs will they have laid altogether?

3) What if the FOUR agents lay slabs that are 9 m x 9 m, 6 m x 6 m, 12 m x 12 m and 4 m x 4 m. What distance will have been paved before they are in line again?

4) How far will they have gone before they are in line for a second time?

Once the next questions are answered the diggers can be called to break up the concrete. To make sure that it's not Sandy who cracks, she's going to need some help.

Smashing work! Completing the Da Vinci Challenge will make sure that the beach stays sandy forever!

Da Vinci files

FOUR agents have FOUR different sized square slabs. The areas of their slabs are 64 m^2, 16 m^2, 49 m^2 and 36 m^2.

1) If they start paving from the same point, how far will they have paved before they are in line again?
2) How many slabs have they laid altogether?

Huxley's Think Tank
Think about multiples of the size of each slab!

MISSION FILE 4:15

Many D.A.F.T. agents make light work!

Time: Late afternoon
Place: British Army headquarters

A group of D.A.F.T. agents have tried to put a dampener on this year's firework festivities by soaking all the fireworks with water. With just five days to go until Bonfire night, General Cods-Wallop has offered to try and save the day… and stop it being a damp squib!

I'm so cross I could explode. What should I do, Da Vinci?
Have a go at the Training Mission to make Bonfire Night go with a bang!

TM

The General has planned a meeting to decide what to do. At the start of the meeting everybody needs to shake hands with each other once. The General must work out how many handshakes will need to take place at the meeting.

1) If there are THREE people at the meeting, how many handshakes will there be?

2) If there are FOUR people at the meeting, how many handshakes will there be?

M1

The meeting is about to close. It will only be a success if you can answer these questions.

1) If there are FIVE people at the meeting, how many handshakes will there be?

2) If there are SIX people at the meeting, how many handshakes will there be?

3) If there are SEVEN people at the meeting, how many handshakes will there be?

4) If there are EIGHT people at the meeting, how many handshakes will there be?

Completing the Da Vinci Challenge will ensure that everyone can enjoy some firework fun on November 5th!

Da Vinci files

Have you noticed any patterns so far?

1) Can you work out the number of handshakes for 10 people?

2) Try to find out more about this specific sequence of numbers. What is this sequence known as?

Huxley's Think Tank
Don't forget that people don't need to shake their own hand. Drawing a diagram might help you here.

MISSION FILE 4:16

Light-fingered light stealers!

Time: Early evening
Place: The Olympic Stadium

Buster Crimes has received a tip-off that a group of D.A.F.T. agents is planning to steal the Olympic torch. Buster will need to guard the flame around-the-clock by using his team of top-notch officers.

How do I stop them stealing the torch, Da Vinci?
Huxley has an Olympic Training Mission for you Buster, jump to it!

TM

THREE officers must work in shifts. They must work then rest, then work then rest for the same number of hours.

ONE officer stands guard for TWO hours then rests for TWO hours before starting again. A SECOND officer stands guard for FIVE hours. A THIRD officer stands guard for SIX hours.

1) If they all start guarding the flame at the same time, how long will it be before there isn't any one watching the flame?

2) How long will it be before all THREE officers start work at the same time?

M1

Buster Crimes needs to organise FOUR officers to work in shifts. They follow the same work and rest pattern as the officers in the Training Mission.

1) Now FOUR officers work for FOUR, EIGHT, TWELVE and SIXTEEN hours before resting. If they all start at the same time, when will they next start work at the same time?

2) How many shifts will the FOUR officers have worked altogether?

Marvellous! If Buster can complete the Da Vinci Challenge, the D.A.F.T. agents will be stopped in their tracks and the Olympic games will be the best ever!

Da Vinci files

FOUR officers work for FOUR, SIX, NINE and TWELVE hours before resting.

1) If they all start at the same time, how long will it be before they next start work at the same time?
2) If they begin at midnight on 1st August, at what time and date will they start work together again?

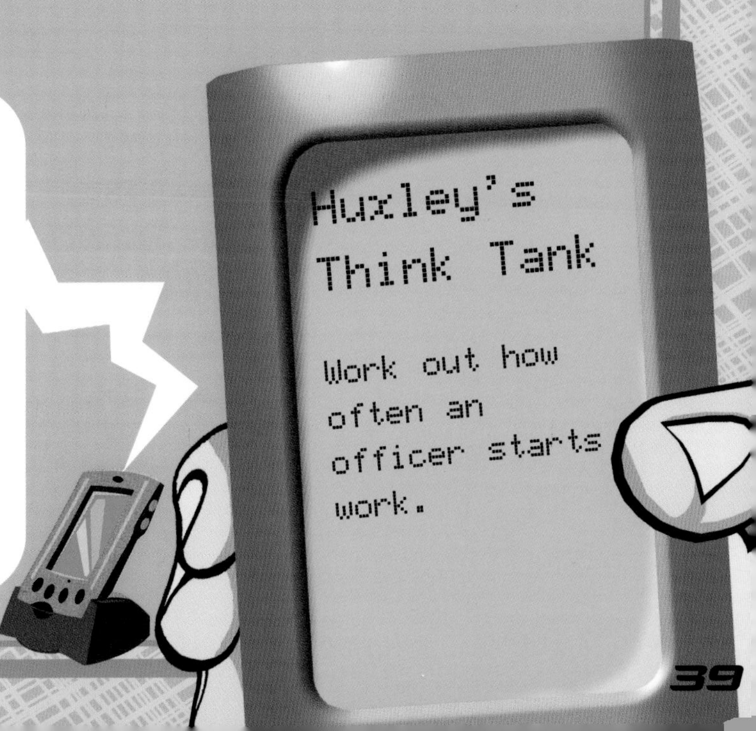
Huxley's Think Tank
Work out how often an officer starts work.

MISSION FILE 4:17

A calculator crisis!

Time: Home time
Place: Hilary's office

Hilary Kumar is very concerned that schools don't have enough money for musical instruments. She is working on a budget to find more funds and will need to show head teachers the facts and figures by Monday… if only her pesky calculator would work!

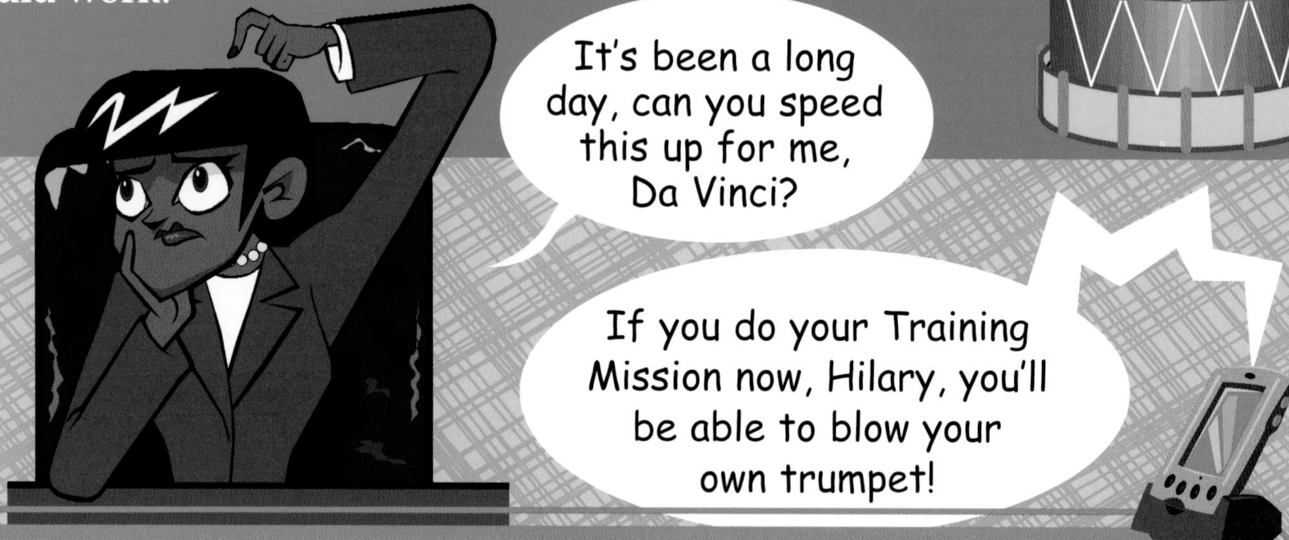

It's been a long day, can you speed this up for me, Da Vinci?
If you do your Training Mission now, Hilary, you'll be able to blow your own trumpet!

TM

Only these buttons work on Hilary's calculator. If she completes the Training Mission she'll be able to write her report before bedtime.

2 3 4 – = +

What sums must Hilary complete so that the answers give her all the numbers between 0 and 10. Investigate as many possibilites as you can.

1) Can Hilary make the numbers 0 to 10 using only these buttons?

2) Now the 2 button has stopped working. Is there a way that Hilary can make the numbers 0 to 10 using only the FIVE remaining buttons?

M1

By investigating further, Hilary can take her report to head teachers and convince them that the music budget should be increased.

0 **9**

Only these buttons are NOT working on Hilary's calculator.

1) How can she use FOUR different single-digit numbers to add up to 20?

2) How many possibilities are there?

Excellent! If Hilary can crack the Da Vinci Challenge all schools will soon be alive with the sound of music!

Da Vinci files

Hilary can use the FOUR operation keys [+ - x ÷] and ONE number key.

Is it possible to make all the numbers from 0 to 10 using any or all of the signs and just ONE number? Start by using just the number ONE.

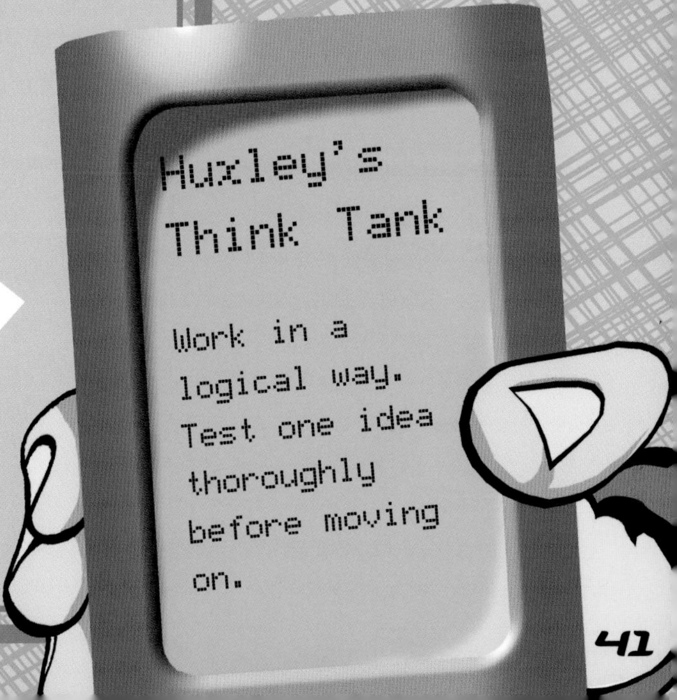

Huxley's Think Tank
Work in a logical way. Test one idea thoroughly before moving on.

MISSION FILE 4:18

A purrr-fect cake for James

Time: Party time
Place: Stella Tiggles' kitchen

It's James Bond's birthday and Stella Tiggles is planning a huge party for her feline friend. She has spent the last week baking him a selection of purrr-fect chocolate cakes and plans to cut them before the guests arrive but she just can't seem to work out how. Time to call Brain Academy!

I need to cut this cake in time for the party.
Huxley has a mouth-watering Training Mission that will make short work of your problem!

TM

One of Stella's cakes is a 10 cm x 10 cm x 10 cm cube. All SIX faces are covered in a scrummy icing. Stella wants to cut the cube into EIGHT smaller cubes measuring 5 cm x 5 cm x 5 cm for her guests to enjoy. Can you help her by answering these questions?

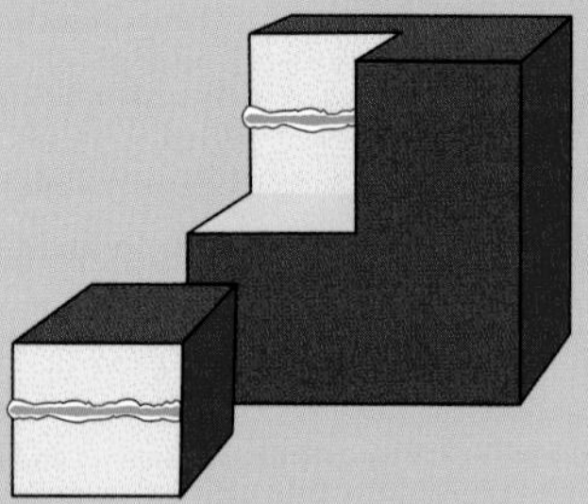

1) When this cake is cut into EIGHT pieces, how many of the cube shaped pieces have icing on THREE faces?
2) How many of the cube shaped pieces have icing on TWO faces?
3) How many of the cube shaped pieces have icing on ONE face?
4) How many of the cube shaped pieces have icing on NO faces?

M1

Completing these questions will mean that the cake that Mrs Tiggles has lovingly prepared and iced on all SIX faces, will be on the table, neatly cut, when the guests arrive.

Mrs Tiggles made a bigger cake that is 15 cm x 15 cm x 15 cm. She ices it and cuts it up in the same way, into pieces measuring 5 cm x 5 cm x 5 cm.

1) How many pieces of cake will she have in total?

2) How many of the cube shaped pieces have icing on TWO faces?

3) How many of the cube shaped pieces have icing on ONE face?

4) How many of the cube shaped pieces have icing on NONE of the faces?

5) How many of the cube shaped pieces have icing on THREE sides?

Great work! Completing the Da Vinci Challenge will mean that the cakes will be eaten up in record time by the hungry guests.

Da Vinci files

Investigate cakes cut into 5 x 5 x 5 cubes that are:

1) 20 cm x 20 cm x 20 cm cubes.

2) 25 cm x 25 cm x 25 cm cubes.

Huxley's Think Tank
Try making the cakes with multilink cubes. You could even ice them with stickers!

Mission Strategies 1

The TASC Problem Solving Wheel

TASC: Thinking Actively in a Social Context

Reflect
What have I learned?

Communicate
Who can I tell?

Evaluate
Did I succeed? Can I think of another way?

Implement
Now let me do it!

Learn from experience
What have I learned?
Communicate
Let's tell someone.
TA
Evaluate
How well did I do?
Let's do it!
Implement

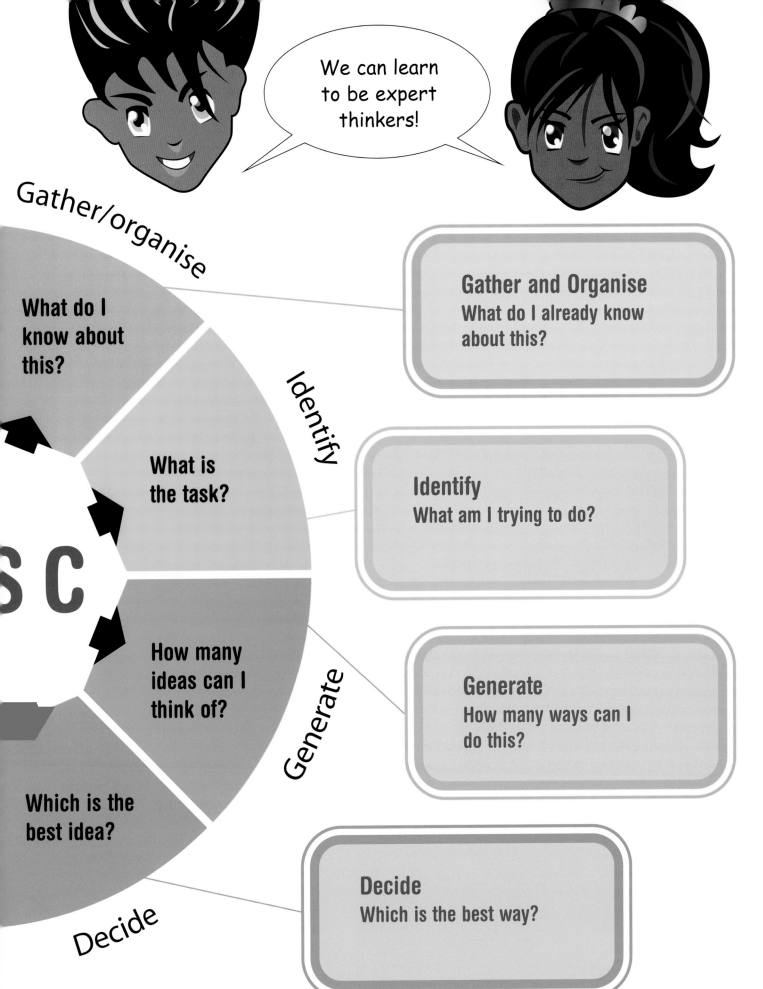

We can learn to be expert thinkers!

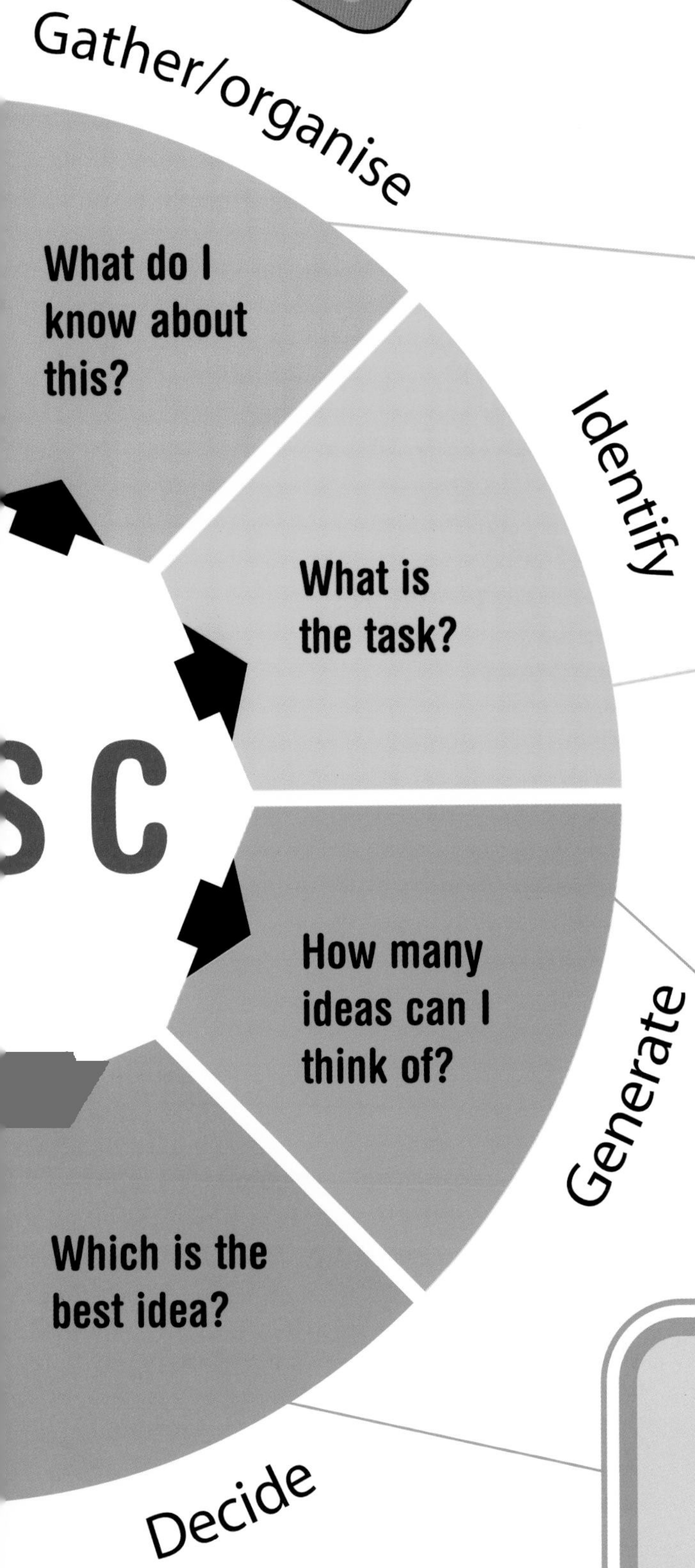
Gather/organise
What do I know about this?
Identify
What is the task?
SC
How many ideas can I think of?
Generate
Which is the best idea?
Decide

Gather and Organise
What do I already know about this?

Identify
What am I trying to do?

Generate
How many ways can I do this?

Decide
Which is the best way?

Mission Strategies 2

MISSION FILE 4:1
Read these questions carefully and write down each piece of information as you work it out. What you have been told about each ingredient will help you answer the questions.

MISSION FILE 4:2
In Mission 1 use B for the number of brothers and S for the number of sisters. Don't forget to include the boy or girl who is in the clue!

MISSION FILE 4:3
In the Da Vinci Files write down what you know about the size of each of the banks from the Training Mission and Mission 1. Then work through the combinations, starting with the simplest.

MISSION FILE 4:4
Remember there are different sizes of right–angled triangles. Use different sizes to make different shapes!

MISSION FILE 4:5
Draw pictures or use different length straws to answer these questions. Don't use metres though, centimetres will do!

MISSION FILE 4:6
Use what you find out in the Training Mission to resolve Mission 1 and the Da Vinci Files. Look for a pattern that will help you solve more questions like these.

MISSION FILE 4:7
KEY CLUE: you can assume that each mechanic, pensioner and astronaut is identical so you don't have to work out too many different solutions.

MISSION FILE 4:8
Use your times tables and knowledge of remainders to solve these Missions. In the Da Vinci Files carefully write down all the information you know.

MISSION FILE 4:9
Decide on the best way to complete this Mission File before you start. You could draw pictures, use toys or even counters.

MISSION FILE 4:10

For the Training Mission, start working out the combinations at 12 o'clock and 1 o'clock and work around from there. Can you find a way of calculating the number of ways without working through all the combinations?

MISSION FILE 4:11

The code is not systematic so you will have to work out each letter as you go. As soon as you know a D.A.F.T. agent's code write it next to his number.

MISSION FILE 4:12

Are there different ways to complete this problem? Look for patterns in your answers which may be easier to spot if you could draw pictures or use tables. Is there any calculation you could do to solve each problem?

MISSION FILE 4:13

Think about the route you found in the Training Mission. Is there anything about this you can use in M1 – such as the shape of the route?

MISSION FILE 4:14

There are lots of words in this mission so it may help to draw a picture of the agents' starting line and start your calculations from this point.

MISSION FILE 4:15

This is a classic! If you can work out the answers to the first two questions on page 28 you should be able to solve the number of handshakes that really big groups of people would need to make.

MISSION FILE 4:16

Using a table will help with this problem. Make a row for each officer and put a tick or a cross next to the hours that each officer worked or didn't work.

MISSION FILE 4:17

The tricky calculations in this mission use the numbers 6, 7, 8 and 9. Remember you can complete one operation, then press equals and then work on the next operation!

MISSION FILE 4:18

The last Mission File is the trickiest. Think about what are you being asked, ie; which pieces are iced? It will help if you get rid of any pieces that AREN'T iced straight away!

nace

What is NACE?

NACE is a charity which was set up in 1984. It is an organisation that supports the teaching of 'more-able' pupils and helps all children find out what they are good at and to do their best.

What does NACE do?

NACE helps teachers by giving them advice, books, materials and training. Many teachers, headteachers, parents and governors join NACE. Members of NACE can use a special website which gives them useful advice, ideas and materials to help children to learn.

NACE helps thousands of schools and teachers every year. It also helps teachers and children in other countries, such as America and China.

How will this book help me?

Brain Academy Maths books challenge and help you to become better at learning and a better mathematician by:

- Thinking of and testing different solutions to problems
- Making connections to what you already know
- Making mistakes and learning from them
- Working with your teacher, by yourself and with others
- Expecting you to get better and to go on to the next book
- Learning skills which you can use in other subjects and out of school

We hope that you enjoy the books!

Write to **RISING STARS** and let us know how the books helped you to learn and what you would like to see in the next books.

RISING STARS

Rising Stars UK Ltd, 22 Grafton Street, London W1S 4EX